Gran

Unit 2 Reader

OBSOLETE

Skills Strand

GRADE

Amplify learning.

Core Knowledge®

Gran's Trips

"When will Gran get here?" Josh asks.

Jen shrugs.

Just then, Josh and Jen see a cab on the street.

"Gran is here!" Jen yells.

When Gran steps from the cab, Josh and Jen run up to get a hug.

"Was the trip fun?" Josh asks.

"Which one?" Gran asks. "I went on three trips!"

"Where to?" asks Josh.

"One was to the Swiss Alps," says Gran. "In the Alps, there were steep cliffs. I went up to the top of one cliff, but it was slick. I fell and had to cling to the rocks!"

"No!" says Jen.

"Yes!" says Gran. "Here is a snap shot."

"What was the next trip?" Josh asks.

"I went to Hong Kong," says Gran.

"What is in Hong Kong?"

"Lots of stuff," says Gran. "In Hong Kong I met a man who sings and has wings on his back."

"No!" says Josh.

"Yes!" says Gran. "Here is a snap shot."

"What was the last trip?" asks Jen.

"I went to the gulf to swim with the eels and feed the fish," says Gran.

"No!" says Jen.

"Yes!" says Gran. "Here is a snap shot."

"Which trip was the best?" Josh asks.

"This one!" Gran says. "The one where I get to see Josh and Jen!"

The Pet

Gran says, "When I was in Hong Kong, I got a pet."

"What can it be?" asks Jen. "Is it a fish?"

"No," says Gran.

"Is it a dog?" asks Josh.

"No," says Gran.

"Is this pet big?" asks Josh.

"Well," says Gran, "he is not big, but he is long."

"Has he got teeth?" asks Josh.

"He has fangs!" says Gran.

"What are fangs?" asks Jen.

Just then, the bell rings.

Gran says, "That must be him!"

Wong from Hong Kong

Jen yells, "Gran, there is a man here with a big crate."

Gran says, "It must be Wong!"

"Who?" asks Jen.

"The pet I got in Hong Kong," says Gran.

"Wong from Hong Kong?" asks Jen.

"Yep!" says Gran.

"But what is this Wong?" asks Josh.

Gran takes the lid off the crate and lifts up a long, black snake.

"Sweet!" says Josh. "Wong is a snake!"

"Eek!" Jen yells. "I am scared of snakes!"

Gran says, "Wong is a safe snake. There are snakes that can kill us, but Wong is not one of them. This is a snake we can pet."

Where Is Wong?

"Help!" Gran yells.

"What is it?" says Jen.

"Wong is not in his crate!" says Gran. "Where is he?"

Jen checks the pots and pans.

"He is not in here!" she yells.
"Check in the den."

Josh checks the den.

"H<u>e</u> is not in h<u>ere</u>," h<u>e</u> yells. "I bet h<u>e</u> went back to Hong Kong!"

Just then, Wong peeks up from a big vase.

"There he is!" says Josh.

Gran runs to Wong and picks him up. She pets the snake. She is glad to see him.

The Swim Meet

Josh and Jen like to swim. They take Gran to their swim meet.

Jen lines up in lane five.

Josh lines up in lane six.

The kids are up on the blocks.

Then there is a beep.

All the kids dive in. Splash!

"Swim!" yells Gran. "Swim fast!"

Josh and Jen swim as fast as they can. They swim and swim. In no time, they make it to the end.

"Did Josh win?" asks Gran. "Did Jen win?"

Josh and Jen wave and smile. They did not win, but they had a lot of fun!

At the Reef

Josh asks Gran what it was like when she went to the reef.

"Well," Gran says, "it was a lot of fun! I made a plan to meet my pal Mike. I had to ride my bike nine miles to the reef to meet Mike."

"That is a long ride!" says Jen.

"When I got there I went on a dive to see the fish and the eels."

"With Mike?" Josh asks.

"No," Gran says. "Mike did not dive with me. He went to hang glide."

"Did he like it?" Jen asks.

"Not so much," Gran says with a smile.

"Why not?" asks Josh. "It must be lots of fun to hang glide."

"Did he crash?" asks Jen.

"No, no," says Gran, "but he did have a bad time. When it was time to land, he hit a hive of bees! He got stung ten times."

"Yikes!" says Jen.

The Bug Glass

"Gran," Jen says, "Josh is mad at me."

"Why is he mad?" Gran asks.

"I broke his bug glass."

"What is a bug glass?"

"A bug glass is something that lets him see bugs and ants up close."

Gran checks the bug glass.

"It is not so bad," she says. "We can fix it with some tape."

"Josh will still be mad," Jen says.

"We can make him a snack," says Gran. "And we can make the ants a snack, as well."

Gran hands Jen some chips and grapes. "Here," she says, "Set those on the big stone in back."

Gran yells, "Snack time!"

Josh runs in and grabs a snack. Gran lets him munch on it. Then she says, "Jen, take Josh to the stone."

Jen grabs Josh by the hand and takes him to the stone. He sees his bug glass. Then he sees a bunch of ants. He picks up the glass and stares at the ants.

Josh smiles. "The ants like those chips!" he says. He hands Jen the glass. "Here!" he says, "Take a peek!"

The Tape

"Gran," Jen asks, "what is that?"

"This is a **tape** deck," Gran says. "And in it is a **tape** with some songs sung by my Gran."

On the **tape** Gran's Gran sings a jazz song. At the end she sings "Pip! Pip! Ting a ling a ling!"

"I **like** th**ose** n**ote**s she sings at the end!" says Jen.

"So do I!" says Gran.

"Gran," says Jen, "we can act like we are in the band and sing the song!"

"OK," says Gran. "Run and get a dress. I will grab those shades I like."

Gran and Jen dress up. Then they sing the song. At the end they sing, "Pip, pip! Ting a ling a ling!"

Fuzz and Mel

The kids are in bed, but they can not sleep.

"Gran!" Josh yells.

Gran peeks in and asks, "What is it?"

"We can not sleep!" says Josh. "We can not sleep."

"Tell us a tale!" says Jen.

"OK," says Gran. "This is the tale of Fuzz and Mel."

47

Once there were two cats named Fuzz and Mel.

Fuzz was a cute cat who did his best to be safe at all times. Mel was a brave cat who had a fast plane.

"Fuzz!" Mel said, "We can take a ride in my plane!"

"Um," Fuzz said, "well . . . the thing is . . . I like to be safe . . . and I am not . . ."

"It is safe," Mel said. "Jump in!"

The plane went up, up, up.

A duck came up next to the plane.

"What a swell duck!" said Fuzz. "And what a swell plane ride! Why was I so scared of a plane ride?"

Just then, Mel made the plane zip from side to side.

Fuzz did not like that. It did not feel safe to him.

Then Mel made the plane dive.

"ZZZZZZZZZZZ!" went the plane as it dove.

"Stop!" said Fuzz, as he held on to the side of the plane. "Not safe! Not safe!"

Mel set the plane back on the land.

Fuzz felt sick. He had the shakes.

"Ug," he said. "That's the last time I ride in a plane with Mel."

The Sweet Shop

"Gran," Josh asks, "did you have a job when you were a kid?"

"I did," says Gran. "My dad had a sweet shop and I had a job in the shop."

"Did you get to make sweets?"

"Yes," says Gran. "I got to make milk shakes, cakes, and gum drops."

"Was it fun?" Josh asks.

"Some of it was fun," says
Gran. "But it was not all fun and
games. I had to sweep and pick
up. And I had to wipe off the
cake case."

"Can you still make cakes?"
asks Jen.

"You bet I can!" says Gran. "Do
you want to make one?"

King and Queen

"Gran," Josh says, "will y<u>ou</u> tell us a t**a**l**e**?"

"Yes!" says Jen. "Tell the <u>one</u> <u>where</u> y<u>ou</u> had to sc**a**r**e** off the mad hog!"

"N<u>o</u>!" says Josh. "Tell the <u>one</u> <u>where</u> y<u>ou</u> w<u>ere</u> on that ship in the wind and w**a**v**e**s!"

"I will tell y<u>ou</u> a t**a**l**e** I m**a**d**e** up," says Gran. This is a t**a**l**e** of a king and his qu**ee**n."

Once there was a queen who felt sad. All she did was sulk and mope.

The king felt sad that his wife was so sad. He made eggs to cheer up the queen. But the queen said the eggs had a bad smell.

The king made a cake. But the queen did not like it.

The king made gum drops. But the queen did not like them.

By this time, the king was not sad. He was mad. He went back to the stove and made a pot of green slop.

"There!" the king said. "This slop is not fit to feed to pigs! The queen will hate it. But so what?"

The king piled some slop on a plate. Then he gave the plate to the queen.

The queen had a bite.

"Mmmm!" she said. "This is the best!"

"Did sh<u>e</u> **like** the gr**ee**n slop?" Jen asks.

"Yep!" says Gran.

"That w<u>a</u>s an odd **tale**!" says Jen.

"Odd but fun!" says Josh.

Gran tucks the kids in. Then Josh and Jen drift off t<u>o</u> sl**ee**p.

The Trip West

"I have m**a**d**e** plans to t**a**k**e** a trip," says Gran. "M_y_ pal Tex has a ranch in the West. It will b_e_ a lot of fun!"

Gran sm**ile**s, but Josh and Jen _are_ sad.

"W_e_ will miss y_ou_!" says Jen.

"_What_ will w_e_ d_o_ h_ere_?" says Josh.

"Well," says Gran, "What if you kids came on the trip with me? Your mom and dad said I can take you with me, if you would like."

"Yes!" the kids yell. "Take us with you! Take us with you!"

Josh and Jen pack their bags. They get in a cab with Gran. Then they get on a plane.

"Will we be safe on this plane?" Jen asks.

"Yes," says Gran. "This will be a safe plane ride, not like the one Fuzz had with Mel."

When the plane lands, Gran rents a van and drives the kids to the ranch.

Tex is there to greet them. He is a big man with a big hat. He shakes hands with Josh and Jen. Then he hugs Gran.

At the ranch there is a mule with packs on his back and bells on his neck.

"That is Sam," says Tex. "He has all the camp stuff in his pack."

"Will we get to camp?" asks Jen.

Tex nods. "Yup. He has your tent on his back!"

Josh and Jen run to Sam. They pet the mule. Sam shakes and his bells ring.

The kids smile.

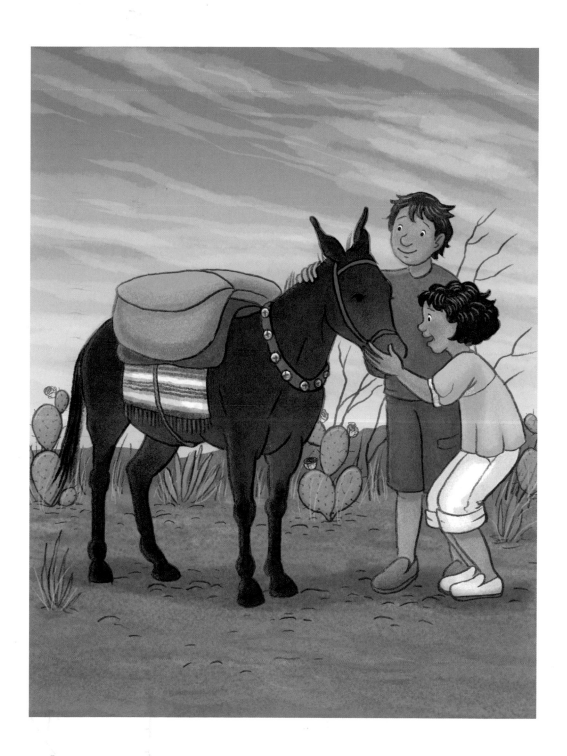

Saved by the Bells

Josh, Jen, and Gran hike off to the camp site with Sam the mule.

"I will meet you there!" Tex yells.

When they get to the camp site, Josh hangs Sam's rope on a tree.

The camp site is close to a cave. Gran and the kids peek in the cave.

Drip. Drip. The cave is damp and dim. No sun shines in the cave.

Josh, Jen, and Gran hike deep in the cave. They get lost. They are a bit scared, but just then Sam's bells ring.

Sam's bells help them get back to the camp site.

When they get back, Jen hugs the mule and says, "Sam, you and your bells saved us!"

Splash Dogs

Tex **take**s Gran and the kids to m**ee**t his dogs, Buck and Pup. Buck is a big black dog. Pup is just a pup.

"We can **take** them to the **lake** so you can s**ee** their tricks," says Tex.

At the **lake**, Tex grabs a stick. "Here, Buck!" he yells.

Tex chucks the stick in the **lake**. Buck runs to the end of the dock and jumps. Splash! Buck swims to the stick and brings it back.

"Can Pup jump?" Jen asks.

"Well," Tex says, "he can swim, but he has not m**a**d**e** a jump yet. Let us s**ee** if w**e** can get him to jump."

Tex t**a**k**e**s a stick and chucks it on the land. Pup runs and gets it. Tex pats him on the back.

Next, Tex t**a**k**e**s a stick and chucks it in the l**a**k**e**. The dogs run off, but Pup skids to a stop at the end of the dock. Buck jumps in and gets the stick.

"This time," Tex says, "keep a hand on Buck and see if Pup will jump."

Gran grabs Buck and hugs him. Tex chucks the stick in the lake. This time, Pup runs and makes the jump. Splash!

Josh and Jen cheer and clap.

Pup pops up and swims back to the land. But what has he got in his teeth?

"Is that the stick?" Josh asks.

"No!" yells Jen. "Pup has a fish!"

Tex and Rex

Josh and Jen s**ee** a man in the den. The man has a black hat.

"Tex!" says Jen.

The kids sm**ile** and w**a**ve. The man w**a**ve**s** back.

"W**e** w**e**re at the cr**ee**k!" Jen yells. The man just sm**ile**s.

"There w**e**re d**ee**r tracks at the cr**ee**k!" Josh yells. The man nods, but then he runs off.

"Gran," Jen asks, "is Tex mad at us?"

"Mad?" Gran asks. "Why?"

"He seems odd," says Jen. "I said we went to the creek and he just smiled."

"And I said there were deer tracks at the creek and all he did was nod," says Josh.

"It was Tex, but he did not act like Tex," says Jen.

Just then, Gran grins. "We need to take a trip to the shed," she says.

When Gran and the kids get to the shed, they see Tex. Then they see the man in the black hat.

Jen stares at Tex and says, "If you are Tex, then who is that?"

"Kids," says Gran with a big smile, "meet Rex. Rex and Tex are twins!"

Gran's Mud Run

Gran, Tex, and the kids <u>are</u> at a track. Gran is <u>a</u>ll set to dri**ve** in a Mud Run. Thr**ee** trucks <u>are</u> li**n**ed up s**id**e b<u>y</u> s**id**e.

A man w**a**v**e**s a flag and the trucks t**a**k**e** off.

Gran is fast. Sh<u>e</u> dri**ve**s past the red truck and the black truck. Sh<u>e</u> spins the t**ir**es and slings lots of mud on the black truck. Splat!

Josh and Jen ch**ee**r.

Gran drives five laps. Then she gets stuck in deep mud.

The red truck speeds by. Then the black one zips past. Gran rocks the truck. It hops from the trench.

Gran steps on the gas. With three laps left, she zips past the black truck.

With one lap left, Gran is just in back of the red truck. The red truck slings lots of mud on Gran's truck. Gran can not see much, but she steps on the gas.

The red truck and Gran's green truck cross the **line side** by **side**.

Gran hops from the truck and yells, "Did I win?"

"Yes!" the kids yell.

Gran w**ipe**s off some mud and asks, "What is my pr**ize**?"

A man runs up with the pr**ize**. He hands Gran a **tire** brush, a big box of rags, and some truck wax.

"Just what I n**ee**d!" says Gran.

Gran's Trip Home

Gran hugs Josh and Jen.

"Tex will **take** you kids back in his truck," she says.

"Will you **take** a bus?" Jen asks.

"N**o**pe," says Gran.

Gran w**ave**s a map. "This will get me h**o**me," she says.

"See here?" she says. "We are here. I will ride my bike to Three Mile Gulch, which is here on my map. It will take me a week to get there."

"A week!" says Josh.

Gran nods.

"I will use my rope to cross the gulch," Gran says. "Then I will hike up to Pine Hill. It's just nine miles."

"Nine miles!" says Josh.

"Then I will be close to home," says Gran. "It is just ten miles from Pine Hill to my home."

"Ten miles!" says Jen.

"You kids have got one heck of a Gran!" says Tex.

As Gran sets off, the kids wave.

Gran waves back. "See you in six weeks!" she yells.

About this Book

This book has been created for use by students learning to read with the Core Knowledge Reading Program. Readability levels are suitable for early readers. The book has also been carefully leveled in terms of its "code load," or the number of spellings used in the stories.

The English writing system is complex. It uses more than 200 spellings to stand for 40-odd sounds. Many sounds can be spelled several different ways, and many spellings can be pronounced several different ways. This book has been designed to make early reading experiences simpler and more productive by using a subset of the available spellings. It uses *only* spellings that students have been taught to sound out as part of their phonics lessons, plus a handful of Tricky Words, which have also been deliberately introduced in the lessons. This means that the stories will be 100% decodable if they are assigned at the proper time.

As the students move through the program, they learn new spellings and the "code load" in the decodable Readers increases gradually. The code load graphic on this page indicates the number of spellings students are expected to know in order to read the first story of the book and the number of spellings students are expected to know in order to read the final stories in the book. The columns on the inside back cover list the specific spellings and Tricky Words students are expected to recognize at the beginning of this Reader. The bullets at the bottom of the inside back cover identify spellings, Tricky Words, and other topics that are introduced gradually in the unit this Reader accompanies.

Visit us on the web at www.coreknowledge.org

CORE KNOWLEDGE LANGUAGE ARTS

SERIES EDITOR-IN-CHIEF
E. D. Hirsch, Jr.

PRESIDENT
Linda Bevilacqua

EDITORIAL STAFF
Carolyn Gosse, Senior Editor - Preschool
Khara Turnbull, Materials Development Manager
Michelle L. Warner, Senior Editor - Listening & Learning

Mick Anderson
Robin Blackshire
Maggie Buchanan
Paula Coyner
Sue Fulton
Sara Hunt
Erin Kist
Robin Luecke
Rosie McCormick
Cynthia Peng
Liz Pettit
Ellen Sadler
Deborah Samley
Diane Auger Smith
Sarah Zelinke

DESIGN AND GRAPHICS STAFF
Scott Ritchie, Creative Director

Kim Berrall
Michael Donegan
Liza Greene
Matt Leech
Bridget Moriarty
Lauren Pack

CONSULTING PROJECT MANAGEMENT SERVICES
ScribeConcepts.com

ADDITIONAL CONSULTING SERVICES
Ang Blanchette
Dorrit Green
Carolyn Pinkerton

ACKNOWLEDGMENTS

These materials are the result of the work, advice, and encouragement of numerous individuals over many years. Some of those singled out here already know the depth of our gratitude; others may be surprised to find themselves thanked publicly for help they gave quietly and generously for the sake of the enterprise alone. To helpers named and unnamed we are deeply grateful.

CONTRIBUTORS TO EARLIER VERSIONS OF THESE MATERIALS

Susan B. Albaugh, Kazuko Ashizawa, Nancy Braier, Kathryn M. Cummings, Michelle De Groot, Diana Espinal, Mary E. Forbes, Michael L. Ford, Ted Hirsch, Danielle Knecht, James K. Lee, Diane Henry Leipzig, Martha G. Mack, Liana Mahoney, Isabel McLean, Steve Morrison, Juliane K. Munson, Elizabeth B. Rasmussen, Laura Tortorelli, Rachael L. Shaw, Sivan B. Sherman, Miriam E. Vidaver, Catherine S. Whittington, Jeannette A. Williams

We would like to extend special recognition to Program Directors Matthew Davis and Souzanne Wright who were instrumental to the early development of this program.

SCHOOLS

We are truly grateful to the teachers, students, and administrators of the following schools for their willingness to field test these materials and for their invaluable advice: Capitol View Elementary, Challenge Foundation Academy (IN), Community Academy Public Charter School, Lake Lure Classical Academy, Lepanto Elementary School, New Holland Core Knowledge Academy, Paramount School of Excellence, Pioneer Challenge Foundation Academy, New York City PS 26R (The Carteret School), PS 30X (Wilton School), PS 50X (Clara Barton School), PS 96Q, PS 102X (Joseph O. Loretan), PS 104Q (The Bays Water), PS 214K (Michael Friedsam), PS 223Q (Lyndon B. Johnson School), PS 308K (Clara Cardwell), PS 333Q (Goldie Maple Academy), Sequoyah Elementary School, South Shore Charter Public School, Spartanburg Charter School, Steed Elementary School, Thomas Jefferson Classical Academy, Three Oaks Elementary, West Manor Elementary.

And a special thanks to the CKLA Pilot Coordinators Anita Henderson, Yasmin Lugo-Hernandez, and Susan Smith, whose suggestions and day-to-day support to teachers using these materials in their classrooms was critical.

CREDITS

Every effort has been taken to trace and acknowledge copyrights. The editors tender their apologies for any accidental infringement where copyright has proved untraceable. They would be pleased to insert the appropriate acknowledgment in any subsequent edition of this publication. Trademarks and trade names are shown in this publication for illustrative purposes only and are the property of their respective owners. The references to trademarks and trade names given herein do not affect their validity.

All photographs are used under license from Shutterstock, Inc. unless otherwise noted.

WRITERS
Kristy Dempsey

ILLUSTRATORS AND IMAGE SOURCES
All illustrations by Apryl Stott